**DES Teacher Education Project
Focus Books**

Series Editor: Trevor Kerry

Effective Questioning

A teaching skills workbook

Trevor Kerry B.A., M.Th., M.Phil.
formerly Co-ordinator, Teacher Education Project,
University of Nottingham

Macmillan Education
London and Basingstoke

First published 1982
Reprinted 1983

Published by
MACMILLAN EDUCATION LIMITED
Houndmills Basingstoke Hampshire RG21 2XS
and London
Associated companies throughout the world

Printed in Hong Kong

CONTENTS

Introduction

PART 1   BASIC QUESTIONING SKILLS   5

Topic 1   Getting pupils to talk constructively   6

Topic 2   Preparing lessons for questioning   6

Topic 3   Asking questions in class – some tactics and strategies   8

Topic 4   Accepting pupils' responses   11

Topic 5   Four questioning skills   12

Topic 6   Higher order questions   15

Topic 7   Written questions   17

Topic 8   Questioning skills reviewed   18

PART 2   CLASSROOM SKILLS WORKBOOK   19

Focus 1   Helping pupils learn through asking questions   19

Focus 2   Structuring lessons for questioning   21

Focus 3   Distributing questions and accepting responses   23

Focus 4   Some questioning skills   25

Focus 5   Practising higher order questions   26

Focus 6   Higher order questions   27

Focus 7   Written questions   29

Focus 8   Assessing your skill as a questioner   32

PART 3   REFLECTIONS ON EXPERIENCE   33

Topic A   Attitudes towards questioning   33

Topic B   Cognitive demands and questioning   34

Topic C   Some questioning skills in more detail   39

Topic D   A transcript for analysis   43

Notes   47

Further reading   48

INTRODUCTION

This is a workbook designed to help teachers and trainee teachers to use questions more effectively in the classroom. It has been constructed in such a way that student teachers can engage in certain activities before, during and after classroom experience. Alternatively, experienced teachers will be able to use it either in the classroom or for study in free time. The workbook is in three parts.

Part 1 contains observation tasks, group discussion and analysis themes and other ideas. It can be used in the early stages of training for students when they may be looking at videotapes, discussing classroom problems, thinking about their role as a teacher or spending a little time in school. Alternatively, it will serve as a systematic introduction to the topic for the more experienced teacher.

In Part 2 there are eight tasks which may be undertaken by the user during a longer block of classroom contact. A mixture of self-analysis and comment by other professionals (tutors, fellow teachers, etc.) is used to sharpen teaching skills and raise awareness about the topic.

Part 3 is best undertaken by students at a later stage in training when substantial classroom experience has been acquired.

ACKNOWLEDGEMENTS

The ideas in this booklet were stimulated by a piece of small-scale research devised by Dr George Brown and Professor E. C. Wragg. Mrs Anna Dennison BEd undertook analysis of the completed research schedules. My thanks are due also to Neville Hatton of Sydney University and to Ted Wragg of Exeter University who commented on the draft. I have made some changes to Part 3 in the light of their comments; but they are not responsible for its faults or omissions.

The author and publishers wish to thank the following who have kindly given permission for the use of copyright material:

Penguin Books Ltd for extracts from *Language, the Learner and the School* by D. Barnes *et al*, published by Penguin Education, revised edition 1971. Copyright © Douglas Barnes, James Britton, Harold Rosen, and The London Association for the Teaching of English, 1969, 1971.
Sydney University Press for an extract from *Sydney Microskills*, Series 2, 1975 by C. Turney, *et al*.

PART 1
BASIC QUESTIONING SKILLS

If, as seems likely, teachers ask about one thousand questions a week, then it follows that questioning is an important aspect of the teacher's teaching skill and of the pupil's learning environment. Yet research has been generally pessimistic about the effectiveness of much of this questioning. Barnes concluded about a series of lessons which he studied:

'Since most questions in the sample were closed-ended, pupils were seldom invited to think aloud, to generate new sequences of thought, to explore implications.'[1]

Pate and Bremer have shown that in the minds of most teachers questions are mainly designed to check pupils' specific recall of facts or to assess whether other kinds of learning have taken place.[2]

In a piece of research at Robin Hood Secondary School, Kerry[3] found that the eight teachers of class 1x asked questions in the proportions shown in the pie chart below (Figure 1).

All three Parts of this booklet suggest that such a vital skill as questioning can be put to more varied and effective uses.

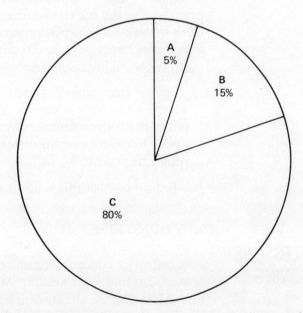

Figure 1   Pie chart of questions asked at Robin Hood school during thirty two lessons

A: higher order questions concerned with analysis, evaluation etc.
B: questions concerned with class management, control or administration.
C: questions of a lower order concerned with data recall or simple comprehension.

TOPIC 1
GETTING PUPILS TO TALK CONSTRUCTIVELY

In asking a question the teacher assumes that a pupil or pupils will respond. If, however, children are used to living in a school system either where pupil talk is not encouraged or where pupil response is characteristically limited to monosyllables, then it will be difficult to use questions effectively as a teaching tool. So a first priority is to encourage pupils to talk. However, let it be emphasised from the outset that pupil talk in this context means *on-task* talk. On-task talk by pupils may be directed to the teacher or to fellow pupils; it may be a response or an initiation. But it is about the job in hand. This booklet is not concerned with the social chit-chat which may oil the works of classroom life (or, in excess, may clog them into a state of seizure).

The teacher needs to set the tone for classroom talk. Many teachers talk too much (a conservative estimate would suggest about 60 per cent of the time). Opportunities need to be provided for pupils to talk back. Of course, teachers who can talk to pupils outside worktime about the local football team, fishing, clothes etc. will signal already that conversation is important. During worktime the casual conversation will have broken the ice so that pupils are more anxious to respond to questions — the idea of talking to and with the teacher will be less foreign. If responses are handled sensitively (more on this subject below) the children will continue to offer ideas. Opportunities can be found for pupils to talk to each other: small groups can work co-operatively on problems.

To emphasise the points which are being made here, Focus 1 in the workbook (page 19) provides the opportunity for a student on teaching practice to break the classroom ice with a group of pupils by signalling to them the value he/she places on talk and its role in learning, and the importance he/she attaches to questions to and from the pupils.

A final word here is probably best left with Hannam:

'Much of (the pupils') creative energy will be absorbed in trying to guess what the teacher's intentions are: they will tend, for example, to give safe rather than adventurous answers, to write correctly rather than imaginatively, to reduce every transaction in the classroom to a mechanical and ritualistic process.'[4]

It is to help combat this attitude that this booklet has been designed.

TOPIC 2
PREPARING LESSONS FOR QUESTIONING

KEY QUESTIONS

As a college of education or university tutor one often reads in students' lesson plans under the heading 'Method of teaching' the single entry: discussion. Clearly, the student has not begun to think out how to get discussion actually started (which questions to ask, which starter materials to show or whether there are shared experiences to draw upon), how to sustain and feed the discussion (by being able to introduce evidence on the subject under review), or how to use it (what knowledge should be gained and in what form pupils should record their knowledge).

The same kinds of comments apply to questioning. A skilful teacher may *appear* to pluck questions out of the air. The reality is probably that a good deal of preparatory thought has been given to finding *key questions* which, *in sequence*, will *lead pupils on to explore new thoughts* and avenues of approach. Of course, the exact form of the following questions will often be modified in the light of responses given to a previous question. Questioning is a skill which does require much thinking 'on one's feet' — you will discover that in Focus 1. But without adequate preparation and forethought an inexperienced questioner will simply fail to pursue a satisfactory train of thought.

Activity 1:
Key questions

Look at the following passage. *Pick out the key questions* in it and list them.

1

2

3

(Check your answer with those on page 45)

'The Bible Library'

Teacher: Why do you think the Bible is sometimes called a library?
Pupil: Because there are so many books in it.
Teacher: That's one reason. Shall we go on and see if we can name some? Daren?
Daren: Kings.
Jane: Mark.
Teacher: Any others?
Alan: Genesis.
Jim: 1 Corinthians.
Teacher: Good. There are lots more. You could look at the contents page for others and add up the total. But there's something more interesting about these many books. Suppose you were a librarian in charge of them, how would you arrange them on your shelves?
Sally: In chronological order, the earliest first.
Teacher: That's certainly one way of doing it. Is that ever done in the Bible?
Sally: Yes, Genesis tells you about the beginning of the world.
Tim: But the chronological sequence doesn't last because all the prophets come together. You could group the books round themes or ideas.
Teacher: If you were a librarian you might use that classification idea. How would that work? Yes, Alan.
Alan: Well, I suppose you'd put all the prophets together, all the Gospels together, all the history books together and so on.
Teacher: Good. That leads us on to labels for some of the other books. How about a label for Job?
Simon: He's a prophet.
Mike: When you told the story of Job, sir, you called the book Wisdom.
Teacher: Well done. If you really want to be technical you could label Job a sort of anti-Wisdom; his friends were the ones who used the Wisdom ideas. Can you give any other examples of Wisdom itself?
Jeff: Ecclesiastes.
Teacher: Good. And what about some more labels?
Ann: Letters, because St. Paul wrote a lot.
Teacher: Any more?

POSING PROBLEMS: AN OPEN-ENDED APPROACH

If you look back at the transcript you will see that the problem in this case was initiated by the question: 'Why do you think the Bible is sometimes called a library?'. In research literature questions are sometimes categorised into two types, 'open' and 'closed'. Closed questions require *either* a monosyllable response *or* a single correct answer where no other will do. Open questions allow for opinion, speculation, the generation of hypotheses, the putting up of an argument. The question which started the transcript was open, so it enabled the pupils to speculate and the teacher to put further questions.

When you introduce lessons in which questioning is a major teaching skill you will need to develop your ability to ask open questions.

FOLLOWING UP LESSONS

Among other things, questions should stimulate curiosity, the desire to know. There is a sense in which curiosity *can never* be satisfied — total knowledge is beyond us, and all our knowledge really consists of short-term working solutions to problems.

In another sense curiosity *should never* be satisfied: it is a motivating factor in learning and should be kept 'on the boil' (this helps to explain the popularity of serial stories and omnibus TV programmes!).

But even so, summaries of our present state of knowledge are important.

How, at the end of a lesson, can one achieve both ends: the summarisation of things learned and the stimulation of sustained curiosity?

Section 4 of Focus 2 suggests a way of doing this. At the end of a lesson either teacher or pupils can sum up what has been learned. There may be many courses of action to this end: writing key points on the blackboard, a quick quiz, a practical test, or giving out an appropriate handout for revision purposes are some of them. On the other hand, the teacher might go one step further and ask a question which puts the whole issue of the lesson on a new level. Instead of closing the subject as if that were the sum total of knowledge this will give some pupils, at least, food for thought. Sometimes this kind of follow-up question can be related to homework, or may be picked up at the start of the next lesson. Learning will then be more of a serial instead of a short, but forgotten, story.

TOPIC 3
ASKING QUESTIONS IN CLASS—SOME TACTICS AND STRATEGIES

It is a fact that teachers constantly signal their requirements to pupils. These signals are often non-verbal, such as nodding and gesture. For this reason perhaps, every training course for teaching should begin with a study of non-verbal cues. Let us consider here for a moment the implications of this for questioning.

When a teacher is standing at the front of the class asking questions, or immersed in a small group of pupils trying to probe their knowledge and lead them on to the next step, he or she is continually inviting response by the verbal form of what is being said. These general signals are reinforced by inflection in the voice in the oral question mark.[5] At the same time the teacher will be looking around the group: without eye contact it is unlikely that pupils will be cued to give a response. For example, raised eyebrows may indicate 'Go on, then' to a hesitant pupil. The class or group will be reading signs about climate: whether the teacher is enthusiastic, encouraging, being humorous or forbidding, or adding a note of censure. For more about non-verbal cues the reader might like to look at Desmond Morris's *Manwatching.*[6]

A specific use of both verbal and non-verbal cues is that of controlling the amount of response each individual makes. Clearly, it would be ideal in most cases if all pupils were to respond to teachers' questions but the dynamics of groups are such that this is rarely the case. Some pupils want to answer everything (they may be clever, highly motivated or precocious); others appear to want to respond to nothing (perhaps they are shy, frightened of scorn if incorrect, or unable to follow the lesson). *Good question technique includes the ability to distribute questions around the class.*

Distribution can be achieved in a number of ways, as we have hinted already. A teacher can encourage the waverer by non-verbal cues, can ask questions to named pupils, or can work systematically around a class (less good, though, because those whose turn is past may tune out!)

In addition, each teacher tends to have a 'zone of maximum interaction' in the classroom. Some have a left-hand or right-hand bias, i.e. they are more conscious of what is happening on one side of the room rather than the other. Others may suffer from tunnel vision. Most are in danger, at least sometimes, of being inhibited by the normal arc of vision (see Figure 2). A few teachers even shut their eyes when they talk — an unforgivable sin — and it will not help class control to look over the pupils' heads.

Figure 2   Normal arc of vision

There is a *tendency* (it is not a scientific rule, and should be applied with caution) for pupils to sit in classrooms in places determined by their degree of interest. Figure 3 shows a typical spread of interest in a classroom.

To be conscious of one's own bias in observing the pupils and of the normal arc of vision, and to be mobile in order to overcome these possible handicaps, will help in the distribution of questions around the class. The exercise in Section 1 of Focus 3 (Part 2) is aimed at discovering problems student teachers may have in these areas. But all this will be to no avail if the teacher, once having persuaded a pupil to respond to his question, fails to accept or use the answer he is given.

Figure 3   Typical spread of interest. A = most involved; D = least involved.

TOPIC 4
ACCEPTING PUPILS' RESPONSES

Consider these short extracts and then carry out the activity:

1   *Teacher*:   We've had a look at how the Romans built roads. Do you know the names of any Roman roads which still exist?
  Pupil: The Fosse Way.
  Teacher: That's right. Do you know where it runs from or where it goes to, Terry?

2   *Teacher*:   What do you feel about this passage? What's the message behind it? Fred?
  Fred: It's a caricature, isn't it?
  Teacher: A caricature? What sort of answer is that? I don't suppose you even know what a caricature is. Answer the question.

3   *Teacher*:   What is a Hittite? John?
  John: A kind of spear?
  Peter: Take no notice of him, sir; he's thick. It's a tribe or nation.
  Teacher: Well done, Peter. Where did the Hittites live?

4   *Teacher*:   What is Kenneth Grahame describing in this passage? Julie?
  Julie: A sort of feeling.
  Teacher: Yes, a sort of feeling. Can you be more exact, Julie. Think of a word to describe the feeling, an adjective to describe it.
  Julie: A mysterious feeling, sort of 'churchy'.
  Teacher: Mystery's a good word. And 'fear'. What little word suggests mystery *and* fear?

Activity 2:
Accepting pupil responses

Which of the teachers whose work is featured in the four extracts above are likely   a)   to encourage pupil participation
             b)   to discourage future responses by pupils?

Jot reasons for your answers in each case.

Extract 1   Teacher encourages future response.   YES/NO
Reasons for answer:

Extract 2   Teacher encourages future response.   YES/NO
Reasons for answer:

Extract 3   Teacher encourages future response.   YES/NO
Reasons for answer:

Extract 4   Teacher encourages future response.   YES/NO
Reasons for answer:

NB: A brief commentary on the four extracts can be found on page 45. Compare your answers with this.

From the Activity and the commentary on the extracts you will have learned something about using pupils' responses. Practise your own acceptance of pupils' responses and ask a fellow-student to analyse your performance by using Section 2 of Focus 3 in Part 2.

TOPIC 5
FOUR QUESTIONING SKILLS

At this point, let us take stock. So far you have considered how to get pupils talking and asking questions, and how to prepare lessons in which questioning is an important feature of teaching skill. You have also looked at ways to distribute questions around the class and how your own behaviour will encourage or discourage responses from pupils. The next few pages examine in more detail some skills in formulating and asking questions and in using questions to bring about thinking at higher cognitive levels. We begin with some quite simple skills, which should require only a little practice for them to become second nature.

VOCABULARY LEVEL AND CLARITY OF EXPRESSION

Obviously a question is not going to perform its function if it is so badly expressed as to be unintelligible. Look, for example, at these questions:

1 What difference does it make if Shakespeare's plays were written by Marlowe?
2 If $y = 2x - 5$, what is y when $x = 7$?
3 What is the meaning of convention?
4 Now, this symbolism we've been talking about, that Eliot has in mind in his play, what kind of role does it play in the totality of everyday life, in the existential 'now'?

Activity 3:
Clarity in questioning

Which of the sample questions given above are clearly expressed? Which are ambiguous or unintelligible? Indicate your response below and give reasons for your verdict.

1 Clear/ambiguous/unintelligible. Reasons:

2 Clear/ambiguous/unintelligible. Reasons:

3 Clear/ambiguous/unintelligible. Reasons:

4 Clear/ambiguous/unintelligible. Reasons:

NB: A commentary on these questions is to be found on page 46.
 Compare your responses with the commentary.

In the same way the level of vocabulary is important. This must be decided in each individual case according to the age and ability of the class being taught. Even one word in a question which is not understood by the pupils will render it incapable of receiving response. So it may be necessary some-times, by preliminary questions, to establish that the pupils are *au fait* with the technical language involved. Thus you may want to ask:

'What effect does migration have on the life-expectancy of passerines?'

But you may be forced back to a series of steps:

Teacher: Who can remember what we called the regular seasonal movement of birds and animals to escape cold weather?

12

Jeff: We called it migration, sir.

Teacher: Yes, Jeff. And what do you think is meant by the term life-expectancy? Sylvia?

Sylvia: Well, it's the length of time a person, or a creature, can hope to live. It's a sort of average length of time that members of a species live for. Humans might expect to live to about 70.

Teacher: Good. Life-expectancy in humans is about 70. Who remembers what life expectancy was among warblers?

Ann: Not much above a year and a bit.

Teacher: That's about right. Now warblers belong to a group of birds which perch. This group has a technical name. The technical name is PASSERINES (Teacher writes on board). Many passerines face a choice: to stay put in a place during bad weather or to migrate. Obviously, if they stay put their life-expectancy is threatened by cold, wet and lack of food supplies. But, suppose they choose to migrate. What effect do you think migration might have on the life expectancy of passerines?

John: Some get killed flying into lighthouses.

Michael: Some die of exhaustion.

Sylvia: It might be less risky to fly the ocean for a little while for a certain meal than hang about in safety for a few weeks and then be short of food in poor weather . . .

TIMING

Some teachers develop a sten-gun mentality spraying questions in all directions, often the same question in many guises. They may be victims of a simple but destructive fault: impatience. A question which demands a thoughtful answer implies that pupils must be given *thinking time*. The new teacher is afraid of silence lest the class take advantage and riot. But there is a happy medium between allowing no time for response and giving the class so much time that they lose interest. Try to read the signs of 'readiness to answer' on pupils' faces, in their eyes or their gestures. Deliver questions in a calm and authoritative way as though you really want to know the answer and you expect to get a sensible one. (There may be exceptions to these suggestions. For example, linguists may use rapid questioning effectively to practise grammar or vocabulary; and mathematicians, too, can sharpen children's thinking in this way.)

REINFORCEMENT

Some tactics you might try include: praising good answers; using pupils' names where possible; building up from half-answers; not rejecting wrong answers (see *Prompting* below). Above all, don't allow pupils to pour scorn on incorrect answers and don't yourself shout at pupils who give a genuine but incorrect response; don't threaten or punish them, don't break into hysterical laughter or indulge in sarcasm. Try using 'yes', nods, qualified approval, or re-phrasing to encourage a child to go on responding or to improve his or her answer.

PROMPTING

Prompting implies that a pupil cannot give a correct response — the question is beyond him. You will then have to prompt or help him by going back two or three steps, and by making your prompting questions simpler. The following would count as an example of prompting.

Teacher: What are the arguments in favour of euthanasia, John?

John: (no response — shrugs)

Teacher: Do you remember what euthanasia is? I broke it up into two parts to explain it: 'EU' meaning 'well' or 'easy' and 'THAN'. What did 'THAN' mean?

John: Death.

Teacher: Good. So what did the whole word mean?

John: Making death easy, like when you're old and very sick.

Teacher: Yes, good. Well, some people believe the end should be made easy, then. Why do they believe that? (etc.)

Activity 4:
Looking at questioning skills

1 Look at the transcript below. Pick out examples of the 4 questioning skills discussed above, and some examples of lack of skill. Jot notes about them in the margin.

2 Compare your notes with the commentary on page 46.

Social Class

Teacher: From the story we've just read, is it possible to decide which social class Colin belongs to? Peter?

Peter: Working class, Miss.

Teacher: Fair enough, but why?

Peter: Well, both his mum and dad work, Miss.

Teacher: 'Working class' does have something to do with 'working', but it's not quite the way you make the link. Anyone?

Marie: It's to do with the kind of job you do. People who work with their hands, doing dirty jobs, bricklayers and car mechanics, they are 'working class'. Clean jobs, like airline pilots and doctors belong to a higher class.

Teacher: You're getting much warmer, Marie. Well done. Now, all of you, stop and think about this — don't rush to answer. What other factors put people into 'working' or 'middle' class according to the Registrar General's classification besides having clean or dirty jobs? I'll jot a list on the blackboard in a couple of minutes . . . Right now; any ideas?

Jo: Money, how much you're paid.

Ann: Perks, and that.

Bill: If you're paid weekly or monthly.

Teacher: What's the difference?
  (No response. Neil goes on with the list.)

Neil: Status.

Teacher: Good word, Neil. What's 'status'?

Ian: My mum shops at Status.

Teacher: If you want to play the goat, go somewhere else. Ann?

Ann: High powered?

Teacher: You're on the right track. Can you put the word in a sentence?

Ann: 'The man was status-conscious'.

Teacher: Yes. So what is he conscious of?

Ann: His own importance?

Teacher: Yes. Not only his importance in his own eyes. What else?

Ann: How other people see him. Their opinion.

Teacher: Good. So status is about how you and other people see 'you', or in our context 'your job'. Can you suggest any high status occupations, Ann?

Ann: Doctor, Nurse.

Teacher: Do high status, high wages and high social class always go together?

Alan: No. My dad says . . .

In Focus 4 you will practise the skills described in this section.

TOPIC 6
HIGHER ORDER QUESTIONS

Some questions demand a higher level of thought from respondents than others. Take just two simple examples:

1 What colour are copper sulphate crystals?
2 Why do you think *Wind in the Willows* has proved such a popular book?

In the first question the pupils are asked to recall a fact taught in a previous lesson. The response to a *data recall question* is often monosyllabic, requires a minimum of teacher-pupil contact and is either correct or incorrect. It will be immediately obvious that, by contrast, the second question has no one 'right' answer (it is an 'open' as opposed to a 'closed' question). Pupils are free to make a variety of responses and they will have to formulate one or more *reasons* into a sentence or so.

Thus, in our examples, question 1 is a lower order question and question 2 is a higher order question.

Activity 5:
Examples of question types

There are a number of ways of categorising question types. Some alternatives are given on pages 38 and 39. For our purposes we have adopted the method set out in Figure 4 (p. 16).

Study the question types set out in Figure 4. Learn each one and practise making up your own examples of each for your own subject area.

Type	Examples
1 Data recall	(a)
	(b)
2 Naming	(a)
	(b)
3 Observation	(a)
	(b)
4 Control	(a)
	(b)
5 Pseudo-question	(a)
	(b)
6 Speculative	(a)
	(b)

7 Reasoning   (a)

                    (b)

8 Discriminatory   (a)

                    (b)

9 Problem-solving (a)

                    (b)

Figure 4   Analysis of Questions

	Question type	Explanation
1	a *data recall* question	Requires the pupil to remember facts, information without putting the information to use, e.g. 'What are the four rules of number?'
2	a *naming* question	Asks the pupil simply to name an event, process, phenomenon etc. without showing insight into how the event etc. is linked to other factors, e.g. 'What do we call the set of bones which cover the lungs?'
3	an *observation* question	Asks pupils to describe what they see without attempting to explain it, e.g. 'What happened when we added litmus solution to hydrochloric acid?'
4	a *control* question	Involves the use of questions to modify pupils' behaviour rather than their learning, e.g. 'Will you sit down, John?'
5	a *pseudo-question*	Is constructed to appear that the teacher will accept more than one response, but in fact he/she has clearly made up his/her mind that this is not so, e.g. 'Do you feel beating slaves was a good thing, then?'
6	a *speculative or hypothesis generating* question	Asks pupils to speculate about the outcome of an hypothetical situation, e.g. 'Imagine a world without trees, how would this affect our lives?'
7	a *reasoning or analysis* question	Asks pupils to give reasons why certain things do or do not happen, e.g. 'What motivates some young people to get involved in soccer violence?
8	an *evaluation* question	Is one which makes a pupil weigh out the 'pros and cons' of a situation or argument, e.g. 'How much evidence is there for the existence of an after-life?'
9	a *problem solving* question	Asks pupils to construct ways of finding out answers to questions, e.g. 'Suppose we wanted to discover what prompts birds to migrate, how could we go about it?'

NB: Question types 1—5 clearly are more 'closed' than types 6—9. Types 1—5 demand shorter answers, less thought and little competence in language use by the pupils. Types 6—9 are clearly more demanding.

In Focus 5 and Focus 6 in Part 2 you will practise using higher order questions. It is unlikely that you will be able to use these exclusively because good questioning tends to run in *sequences*.

A sequence of questions builds up from lower order to higher order, making progressive demands on pupils' thinking. After you have practised using higher order questions in Focus 5, something of this sequential pattern should emerge in Section 2 of Focus 6.

TOPIC 7
WRITTEN QUESTIONS

Whenever you set a written exercise, a test or a piece of homework you are, in effect, asking questions. Many of these questions are written questions — you put them on the blackboard, cull them out of books or have them duplicated on exam sheets. Pupils respond to them in writing. Nevertheless they should be subject to the same scrutiny, and achieve the same ends, as oral questions. In Focus 7 you will have a chance to review your written questions and pupils' written responses.

Activity 6:
Looking at written questions

Gather together some commercial or 'home-produced' worksheets in your subject area. Look at the questions in the light of Figure 4 and of what you have learned in this unit.

Ask yourself whether the questions are clear and unambiguous.

Study the questions on the pattern laid out in Figure 4.

Activity 7:
The purpose of written questions

Having studied questions from the worksheets, set out below some reasons for setting written questions in class or for homework. What purpose do they serve?

1

2

3

4

How do some written questions which you have used differ from those found in the worksheets:

   (a)   in purpose
   (b)   in style?

(a) 1   (b) 1

      2   2

      3   3

      4   4

When you mark pupils' responses to written questions set as classwork or homework what kinds of comments do you write on the responses and what purpose do these comments serve?

If possible, add photocopies of some pupils' marked work to this booklet in order to illustrate the points you make.

TOPIC 8
QUESTIONING SKILLS REVIEWED

Throughout Part 1 of this booklet we have been concerned with a range of skills which (student) teachers can acquire to help them ask more effective questions. A short list would be:

1 Pitching the language and content level of questions appropriately for the class.
2 Distributing questions around the class.
3 Prompting and giving clues when necessary.
4 Using pupils' responses (even incorrect ones) in a positive way.
5 Timing questions and pauses between questions.
6 Learning to make progressively greater cognitive demands through sequences of higher order questions.
7 Using written questions effectively.

Focus 8 in Part 2 puts this whole range of skills to the test by asking a tutor to watch you at work and to comment under each of the seven headings.

This exercise is likely to be of great value in helping you to assess progress; but you can always repeat the process at any time by tape-recording your own lesson and becoming your own armchair critic in the privacy of your own home.

PART 2
CLASSROOM SKILLS WORKBOOK

Part 2 of this workbook contains eight exercises designed to help you improve your skills. The exercises are spread over four weeks of intensive practice. However, you can alter this timing to fit in with your teaching practice if you are a student or your normal workload if you are a probationer or qualified teacher. Below is an outline plan of the workbook. For students the best time to do the work is during the second half of teaching practice, when you will know the pupils better and they will be more at ease with you.

Focus	Topic	Who does this*	When to do it	Tick when complete
1	Helping pupils learn through questions	You A fellow student	Week 1 first half	
2	Structuring lessons for questioning	You	Week 1 second half	
3	Distributing questions and accepting responses	A fellow student	Week 2 first half	
4	Some questioning skills	Co-tutor	Week 2 second half	
5	Practising higher order questions	Co-tutor	Week 3 first half	
6	Higher order questions	Tutor	Week 3 second half	
7	Written questions	You	Week 4 first half	
8	Assessing your skill as a questioner	Tutor	Week 4 second half	

*Students will be able to use a variety of observers; qualified teachers may find it helpful to enlist the aid of a colleague where an observer is required

FOCUS 1
HELPING PUPILS LEARN THROUGH ASKING QUESTIONS

WHEN TO DO THIS: During week 1, first half.

WHO DOES THIS: A fellow student (Section 2) and you (Section 3).

WHAT TO DO: For about half of a lesson set up one of the games in Section 1 overleaf. While it is in progress get your fellow student to fill in Section 2. Then carry on with the rest of Section 1.

SECTION 1 A QUESTIONING GAME

The purpose of this exercise is to encourage as many pupils as possible to talk to you, for you to show them that questions in the classroom are valued and to get you to think out basic strategies for setting up problem situations.

A Classroom Game

Either: set up a problem such as placing a mystery object under a cover. Tell pupils that they can find out the identity of the object only when they have deduced correctly what it is. To do this, get them to ask questions of you. Make your responses only 'Yes' or 'No'. They will then be forced to ask progressively specific questions which eliminate ambiguities.

Or: play your own version of Twenty Questions, the only clues to the mystery objects being 'animal', 'vegetable' or 'mineral'.

While the game is in progress try to help the pupils improve their own questioning skills. Praise questions which show insight.

Now change roles; let the pupils set you a problem and you use questions to solve it.

After the game

Show the pupils how a series of questions can help solve problems in your own subject area e.g.

how they could approach testing a hypothesis in science

or how they might solve a problem in mathematics

or how they can decide about a point of grammar in English (e.g. where to place apostrophe) by asking themselves sensible, appropriate questions.

Give an actual example and explain to them why you want them to ask questions and to answer yours in future lessons.

SECTION 2 EXAMINING THE QUESTIONING GAME

While the exercise is in progress your fellow student fills this in:

(a)   How many pupils   (i)   get involved in the game
                                     (ii)   fail to get involved in the game

(b)   Select and record below two or three examples of the teacher helping a pupil to re-formulate a question into an improved form.

(c)   To what extent did the teacher know and use individuals' names in answering the questions?

SECTION 3 FILL THIS IN YOURSELF (your impressions)

How did you feel during the second part of the game, when you were asking the questions? Did you find it easy to 'think on your feet' in this way?

Does this experience suggest any ways of helping pupils to ask questions more easily?

FOLLOW-UP

1 Discuss the findings in Section 2 (above) with your fellow student.

2 Were the class responsive to you? If not, try to discover why this was so.

FOCUS 2 STRUCTURING LESSONS FOR QUESTIONING

WHEN TO DO THIS: During week 1, second half.

WHO DOES THIS: You do.

WHAT TO DO: The Sections below form a planning guide which will help you prepare a lesson using questioning as a teaching skill. Teach the lesson and then carry out the follow-up activity.

SECTION 1 SELECT YOUR TOPIC

Choose a topic which lends itself to a problem-solving approach. Eg:

Why did Hadrian build his wall on its present site?
How could one discover the formula that circumference = $2\pi r$?
What kind of life might people be living in the year 2000?

Write your chosen topic here:

SECTION 2 FORMULATE KEY QUESTIONS

In order to pursue the problem outlined in your chosen topic pupils will need to take systematic steps of reasoning. You will be able to guide their progress by asking *key questions* in the *correct order*.

Plan your key questions here:

1

2

3

4

5

SECTION 3 INTRODUCING THE PROBLEM

In order to get the pupils thinking effectively about the solution to your problem you will need to introduce it to them in the form of a question. This question must pose the problem itself or some important aspect of it. It must be clear, precise and open (i.e. allow pupils to speculate).

Prepare your opening question here:

SECTION 4 SUMMARISING THE LEARNING and ASKING AN EXTENSION QUESTION

During the lesson many pupils should have contributed answers to your questions. It is necessary for you to draw together the threads towards the end of the lesson. Two activities will be helpful at this stage. *In the first place*, you should prepare a summary statement on the blackboard or on a handout, or ask pupils to write their own. *Secondly*, you should try to send pupils away with an *extension question* in their minds — one which takes the problem a stage further (e.g. 'Given what we have discovered about bird migration how would you account for the irregular migration of lemmings?').

Record here:
(a)   What you (or some of your pupils) included in the summary statement:

(b)   Your extension question:

FOLLOW-UP

1   Assess the quality of this lesson either from the pupils' oral responses or their written summaries. Jot notes below about either of these:

2   Did you use the planned questions
      a)   as intended   b)   in a modified form   c)   not at all?

3   Can you think of any questions which you improvised, i.e. thought of as the lesson progressed? If so, jot a few notes here:
      Question:

      Comment:

FOCUS 3

DISTRIBUTING QUESTIONS AND ACCEPTING RESPONSES

WHEN TO DO THIS: During week 2 first half

WHO DOES THIS: A fellow student.

WHAT TO DO: Teach a lesson based on questioning similar to that in Focus 2. Ask a fellow student to watch the whole lesson and fill in Sections 1 and 2 below.

SECTION 1 DISTRIBUTING QUESTIONS
(While you are teaching ask your *fellow student* to fill in the section below.)

Jot a quick seating plan of the class in the box below. During the first twenty minutes of the lesson, each time a pupil answers a question tick the appropriate box by his seat thus:

SECTION 2 ACCEPTING PUPILS' RESPONSES
(Your *fellow student* fills in this section.)

For the remainder of the lesson try to record how the teacher handles pupils' responses to his/her questions. Do this by recording the pupil's response to each question and then the teacher's next comment thus:

	Teacher's question	Pupil's response	Teacher's reaction
1	Why do you think sociologists describe ours as a 'mobile society'?	One reason is that people can move house easily nowadays.	That's a good point that no-one else has raised. Can we take the idea a stage further?
2	Now I'm adding the indicator — what colour is it going?	The liquid is turning blue, sir.	Are you colour-blind, Nick?

	Teacher's question	Pupil's response	Teacher's reaction
1			
2			

FOLLOW-UP

1   Look at the distribution grid. How effectively were you distributing your questions? If you were not sharing them out, why was this? What strategies can you devise to overcome the problem?

2   Are you accepting pupils' answers and using them effectively? Do you sometimes deter people from making further responses? Discuss this with your fellow-student.

3   Do the findings in Section 2 throw any light on your distribution patterns in Section 1?

FOCUS 4
SOME QUESTIONING SKILLS

WHEN TO DO THIS: Week 2, second half.

WHO DOES THIS: Your co-tutor (teacher) does.

WHAT TO DO: Teach a lesson in which questioning plays an important role. Ask your class teacher to watch you at work and fill in the sections below. Before the lesson give the teacher an opportunity to read Section 1.

SECTION 1 QUESTIONING SKILLS
(To be carried out by the class teacher.)

Below are four questioning skills and the common faults associated with them. Become familiar with these and then observe your student at work, filling in Section 2 as you do so.

(a)   *Vocabulary level and clarity*: as in all teaching, so in questioning; what the teacher says needs to be pitched at the right level. Questions must be phrased so as to make sense and not to be ambiguous.

(b)   *Timing*: among common faults in questioning are failure to wait long enough for an answer, seizing too quickly on the first thing a pupil says without giving him or her time to develop it, or asking several questions on end without pausing for a response.

(c)   *Reinforcement*: this implies the ability to praise good answers and to develop half answers. It suggests that teachers should avoid sarcasm and making pupils feel rejected, or other responses which reduce a pupil's wish to make a contribution. (Not all educationists agree that reinforcement is an unqualified virtue — for example, you might read the work of Lawrence Stenhouse (1967) in *Discipline in Schools*, Pergamon Press.)

(d)   *Prompting*: this includes encouragement of pupils who reply to questions with 'I don't know' or 'I'm not sure' etc. The teacher can help the pupil by giving clues or by going back a step or two and asking one or more simple factual questions with which the pupil may feel more secure. Thus the pupil is led towards an answer.

SECTION 2 OBSERVING QUESTIONING SKILLS
(To be carried out by the class teacher.)

Watch the student teacher at work during the course of a lesson and record his performance (good and bad, with short examples) under each of the following skills headings. Record examples of *both good and bad* performance under each heading.

(a)   Vocabulary and clarity

(b)   Timing

(c)   Reinforcement

(d)   Prompting

FOLLOW-UP

1   Discuss with the teacher the skills displayed above, and the occasions when these skills were not shown.

2   Later in the term try to tape-record one of your own lessons. Play the tape back in private and rate yourself under the four headings above. Do you feel your questioning skill has improved in any way?

FOCUS 5
PRACTISING HIGHER ORDER QUESTIONS

WHEN TO DO THIS: During week 3, first half.

WHO DOES THIS: Your class teacher.

WHAT TO DO: Teach a lesson using the question techniques suggested below. Ask your class teacher to watch the lesson and fill in Sections 2 and 3. You will need to give the teacher a copy of your planned key questions BEFORE the lesson.

SECTION 1 PLANNING FOR HIGHER ORDER QUESTIONING

1   *Revise* your knowledge of the categories of question listed below (refer back to page 16).

> speculative or hypothesis generating question
> reasoning or analysis question
> evaluation question
> problem solving question

2   Plan a lesson using at least three of these higher order question types (among others). Write your planned key questions here.
  (i)

  (ii)

  (iii)

3   Finish preparing your lesson and teach it to the class.

SECTION 2 PUPILS' RESPONSES TO HIGHER ORDER QUESTIONS
(Your class teacher fills this in.)

Record below some of the pupils' responses to the three planned key questions.

1

2

3

SECTION 3 USING SEQUENCES OF QUESTIONS IN A LESSON
(Your class teacher fills this in.)

Comment on how effectively the three key questions built up into a sequence. Say how the pupils were, or were not, able to build their thinking progressively through the sequence towards a solution to the problem in hand. Did the sequence of key questions seemed forced or artificial in retrospect, or did they appear to emerge naturally during the course of the lesson?

FOLLOW-UP

1   Discuss the findings in Sections 2 and 3 above with your class teacher.

FOCUS 6
HIGHER ORDER
QUESTIONS

WHEN TO DO THIS:	Week 3, second half.
WHO DOES THIS:	Your tutor does.
WHAT TO DO:	Teach a lesson in which questioning plays a major and varied role. Ask your tutor to use the scheme below to assess the cognitive level of your questions throughout the lesson.

SECTION 1 HIGH AND LOW ORDER QUESTIONS

Your tutor should read the analysis of question types (Figure 4) on page 16 then proceed to Section 2.

SECTION 2 ASSESSING THE COGNITIVE DEMANDS OF QUESTIONS

Record as shown below a brief outline of each question asked during the lesson and place opposite it an analysis of question type (1 to 9) based on the scheme printed on page 16.

Brief Outline   Question Type

Question 1

Question 2

Question 3 (etc.)

FOLLOW-UP

1   Review your questions with your tutor. How many were higher order questions? Look at the way in which your sequences of questions build up.

2   Discuss with your tutor how you might improve your technique of asking higher order questions (the examples recorded above will help to bring to mind specific problems).

FOCUS 7
WRITTEN QUESTIONS

WHEN TO DO THIS: Week 4, first half.

WHO DOES THIS: You do.

WHAT TO DO: Read the preamble in Section 1 and then carry out the exercises in the following Sections.

SECTION 1   WRITTEN QUESTIONS

Whenever you set a written exercise, a test, an examination or a piece of homework you are, in effect, asking questions. Many of these questions are written questions — you put them on the blackboard, cull them out of books or duplicate them on exam sheets. Pupils respond to them in writing. Nevertheless, they should be subject to the same scrutiny, and achieve the same ends, as oral questions. In this Focus you have a chance to review your written questions and pupils' written responses.

SECTION 2   THE PURPOSE OF WRITTEN QUESTIONS

(a)   Suggest four or five reasons why it may be preferable sometimes to set written questions.

(b)   When you set written questions do you expect different kinds of responses from when you ask oral questions? List some ways in which you think the responses should differ.

SECTION 3 JUDGING THE QUALITY OF WRITTEN QUESTIONS

Look back over some written questions you have set in the last few weeks.
Record some of them below and suggest why you felt that they were
valuable exercises. Record also any reservations you now have about them
in the light of your answers in Section 2.

Questions   Observations

1

2

3

SECTION 4 JUDGING PUPILS' ANSWERS

Select just one of the written questions recorded in Section 3 on page 30.
Look back over pupils' responses to it. Record below
(a) any problems they had in answering the question and
(b) some good points which they made in response.

(a) Problems   (b) Good Points

(Staple to the booklet a photocopy of the best and worst answers if you
can.)

FOLLOW-UP

How can you improve on your use of written questions and pupils' answers?
Jot any ideas you have about this in the space below. Here are some headings
to help you.

Purpose   Are the questions set for revision, to help pupils discover new
information, to allow them to practise some principles, or for other purposes
(specify)?

Clarity and language level   Are the questions clear in form and in vocabulary? Is the language of the questions appropriate?

Thinking level   Are the questions set too exacting or insufficiently demanding? Are the demands made suitable for average pupils, for bright and slow
learners?

Information   Does the child have all the information required in order to
answer the questions? If not, how can he find it?

Instructions   Have you made it clear when the work should be finished,
how much time should be spent on it, and how and where the answers
should be written?

FOCUS 8

ASSESSING YOUR SKILL AS A QUESTIONER

WHEN TO DO THIS: During week 4, second half.

WHO DOES THIS: Your tutor.

WHAT TO DO: Teach a lesson in which questioning plays an integral part. Ask your tutor to fill in a lesson evaluation sheet of the kind indicated below.

Lesson Evaluation

TOPIC: CLASS:

LESSON INTRODUCTION AND GENERAL PRESENTATION

ORAL QUESTIONING SKILLS:

(Comment specifically on each of the following questioning skills.)

1   *Language level of questions*

2   *Distribution of questions around class*

3   *Prompting and giving clues*

4   *Using pupils' responses*

5   *Timing*

6   *Cognitive demands made*

VALUE OF ANY WRITTEN QUESTIONS SET

OTHER POINTS OF NOTE ABOUT THE LESSON

FOLLOW-UP

Discuss this lesson evaluation with your tutor. What points need further improvement?

PART 3
REFLECTIONS ON EXPERIENCE

TOPIC A
ATTITUDES TOWARDS QUESTIONING

Activity 8:
Attitudes towards
questioning

Now that you have studied questioning skill and practised it in the classroom, you can pause a while to reflect on your experiences. Below are a collection of short extracts from various writers on the theme of questioning skill.

(a) Take each extract in turn and compare it with what happened in your own classroom.
(b) To what extent do you agree with the sentiments expressed in each of these extracts?

Extract 1: Why questioning?

'When problems of the future can no longer be anticipated and mass persuasion techniques exert a greater influence on the public than ever before, people must be able to think toward responsible choices and decisions. Educators must develop skills for evaluating cognitive levels of thought and methods of raising the cognitive levels at which children function.'

(Rogers, V. M., 1972, 'Modifying Questioning Strategies of Teachers', *The Journal of Teacher Education* 23.1.

Extract 2: Learning to persevere.

'In attempting to help children reach for high levels of thought, many teachers experience considerable frustration and even exasperation because pupil responses remain at a low and unsophisticated level.'

(Turney, C. *et al*, 1975, *Sydney Micro Skills Series 2*.)

Extract 3: Individual pupil differences.

'Whatever the age of pupils there will always be a very large range of individual differences within a group in ways of thinking, interests, and pace of thinking.'

(Turney, 1975)

Extract 4: Comprehension questions

'Though comprehension questions are sometimes regarded as demanding only a relatively simple level of thinking, they can in fact involve a pupil in quite difficult tasks.'

(Turney, 1975)

Extract 5: Thinking time

Part of the teacher's skill is to match amounts of time for responding, to the complexity of each individual question.

Extract 6: Measuring participation

'It is not easy to measure pupil participation, especially since it is the quality of participation which matters rather than its vociferousness.'

(Barnes, D. *et al*, 1969, *Language, the learner and the school*, Penguin)

Extract 7: The learner's role

One interesting facet of the classroom 'relates to the ways in which the teacher covertly signals to his pupils what their role as learners is to be'.

(Barnes, 1969)

Extract 8: Verbalising learning

'A study of closed and open questions would throw light on the problem of dealing with private misconceptions, and upon the value of discussion. What is the value of encouraging pupils to 'think aloud' at length? What importance should be given to insisting that pupils make explicit what they have learned either outside school, or in non-verbal terms inside school?'

(Barnes, 1969)

Extract 9: Word becomes thought

'I believe also that the movement in words from what might *describe* a particular event to a generalization that might *explain* that event is a journey that each (pupil) must be capable of taking for himself — *and that it is by means of taking it in speech that we learn to take it in thought*.'

(James Britton in Barnes, 1969)

Extract 10: Practices to be avoided

(a) Repeating one's own questions.
(b) Repeating pupil answers.
(c) Answering one's own questions.
(d) Questioning for chorus answering.

(Based on Turney, 1975)

Extract 11: A philosophy of teaching

'Questioning is one of the best ways for you to express humanistic attitudes involving respect for (pupils') ideas, freedom of choice, self-expression and honesty . . . Most suggested approaches to teaching today encourage the teacher to act as a guide to learning. One does this primarily through questioning.'

(Roger Cunningham in Weigand, J., 1977, *Implementing teacher competencies*, Prentice Hall)

TOPIC B
COGNITIVE DEMANDS AND QUESTIONING

Great emphasis has been placed throughout this workbook on the cognitive demand made by teachers on pupils, especially through the use of higher order questions. It is now appropriate to consider this issue in a little more detail.

THE NATURE OF KNOWLEDGE

Everything that has been said so far rests upon a number of premises. First, that it is possible to look objectively at classroom transactions. Secondly, that some transactions require pupils to think more deeply than others. Thirdly, the value judgment is made that such 'thinking skills' are important, indeed central, to the purpose of school learning. Finally, it is assumed that the professional training of teachers should make them aware of their own performance skills and of their duty to improve pupils' thinking skills.

Anyone who rejects these premises will find the rest of this workbook irrelevant. For those who accept them the next step is to look at a possible model of knowledge.

Eggleston pictures knowledge in pyramidal form.[7] At the base of the pyramid are those parts of knowledge characterised by information, data or facts.

The second layer of the pyramid consists of what the mind does to draw out simple patterns from facts. This level is the concept level, where one would expect to find simple laws (such as the area of a circle $= \pi r^2$), reasons or explanations.

On the third and highest layer groups of concepts fuse together into principles or abstract entities.

A simple illustration of this theme is made in the following paragraphs which describe a 'thought-route' through a particular learning experience for some pupils:

'The youngsters were taken on a nature walk. Among the creatures they observed were those who made their living along the stream, including the pied wagtails. The teacher asked the pupils to describe the behaviour of some of the creatures observed, and Michael recorded that "wagtails are very busy; they run after insects, and even when otherwise at rest they flick their tails up and down".

'A number of youngsters wrote good observational studies of the wild creatures. There were the rabbits which burrowed into the stream bank and showed white scuts when running away from the observer; there were butterflies with "eyes" on their wings; and there were goldfinch flocks, their wing bars flashing each time the flock moved on.

'The teacher culled out these observations and asked what they had in common. When she had elicited words like "danger", "warning", and "signal" she began to ask why the pupils thought animals had these devices and reached the concept "communication".

'After a while she began to move towards responses in which key words were "develop", "over a long period", "survival". Eventually she arrived at something resembling an account of adaptation and evolutionary development.'

This greatly truncated account of the flow of a series of lessons illustrates Eggleston's pyramid. The pupils began with observational data (wagtails wag their tails, rabbits have white scuts); progressed to concepts (animals use colour and plumage to deter attackers, warn others to flee, communicate their whereabouts); and ended with a theoretical framework or abstract principle (evolution).

The knowledge pyramid is a useful concept. It raises one important question: What are the ideal or desirable proportions of the pyramid? Or, to put it another way: how much data do you need before you can begin to move up the thinking hierarchy?

THE NATURE OF TEACHERS' QUESTIONS

The question just posed is answered implicitly by teachers in the relative number of questions they ask which fall to lower and higher orders. Research has shown over and over again that, of teachers' questions, the predominating ones are those concerned with simple data and the recall of facts already learned. This has been true for the last sixty years, and may be a measure of how little real progress has been made in raising educational standards. Thus Stevens found in 1912 that 65 per cent of questions by teachers in American high schools demanded only the recall of information from text books.[8]

Haynes in 1935 found that 77 per cent of questions asked in history lessons were questions of fact[9]; and Floyd (in 1960) found that even teachers specially selected as 'good' asked 42 per cent data recall questions as opposed to 20 per cent requiring thoughtful answers.[10] In 1965 Gallagher recorded more than half the questions asked of able pupils as being concerned with recall.[11] A recent study of RE teachers showed that, in this most abstract of school subjects, out of exactly four hundred questions asked in the study school by RE staff 79 per cent were lower order questions.[12]

Gall suggests three explanations as to why lower order questions feature so prominently.[13] The first is that of Eggleston's pyramid: teachers need to be sure pupils have a basis of fact before they progress to speculation or higher levels of thought.

The second explanation is that thought-objectives (as opposed to fact acquisition objectives) have come to be written into the curriculum only slowly. Finally, Gall suggests that teachers simply do not possess the skills to ask higher level questions.

This workbook accepts that the last two reasons are important; and it contests the first only so far as it would change the shape of the pyramid. Figure 5 shows two possible knowledge pyramids. Pyramid A reflects a situation as teachers assume it to be. Pyramid B is an equally valid model, and more desirable.

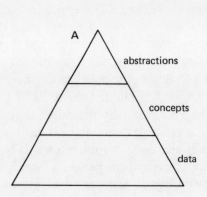 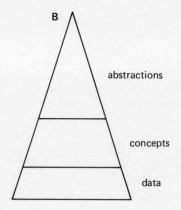

Figure 5   Knowledge pyramids

Perhaps Gall's reasons need some augmentation. Above all, two factors have worked in the last decade against higher order questioning in class-rooms. The rapid rise in mixed ability organisation has meant that teachers frequently aim lessons towards or below the average level for the class[14]. They are thus more reluctant to ask questions designed to provoke thought, and feel more secure with data-based activities in which the progress of all pupils can be measured against a common background.

Since the demise of grammar schools there has been an increased reluctance to give attention to those aspects of education or teaching skills which may appear to be élitist because of their beneficial effects upon the more able. Asking higher order questions is just one of the strategies which may be seen as undesirable by those who hold socio-political rather than educational ideals to be paramount in the classroom.

HIGHER ORDER QUESTIONS AND PUPIL LEARNING

But do higher order questions really help pupils to think more effectively? Most research suggests that they do, though not all of it is free of criticism, and some has been methodologically suspect. Turney has made a good summary of the research.[15]

The important response to the issue of the value of higher order questions seems to lie well back in the education process, at the point where one formulates aims and objectives for education. At root it comes to this: if one formulates into one's aims and objectives for a lesson, course, or school career the higher level thinking skills as well as lower level knowledge of information, then higher order questions will help the pupil towards achieving both low and high level understanding. If one is satisfied with data recall as the end-product of education then any workbook such as this loses its purpose.

HIGHER ORDER QUESTIONS AND PUBLIC EXAMINATIONS

Many teachers maintain that their lack of interest in higher order questioning stems from the failure of public examination syllabuses to include opportunities to use higher level thinking skills, and of the examinations to reward answers which are thoughtful rather than accurate. There can be little doubt that this is partly true, at least up to C.S.E. and G.C.E. 'O' level; and pressure to get through a syllabus does limit the time a teacher can spare for more provocative activities. However, it seems likely that pupils' interest will be better sustained if they are made to think more deeply rather than simply remember and regurgitate. This was the finding of Dunbar in American schools.[16]

This decade more and more schools have put off the moment for serious embarkation upon an examination syllabus into year four. Various long-standing curriculum developments such as science 5–13, Nuffield science, the Humanities Curriculum Project and SMP have, implicitly or explicitly, included opportunities for higher order questions and high level thinking. There is no legitimate reason why pupils should not be appraised of the value of thinking skills from the moment they enter into secondary school — and arguably before that for both the more able and even the average.

TAXONOMIES OF QUESTION TYPES

In Parts 1 and 2 of this workbook you used a nine-category taxonomy of question types. There are many different ways to categorise and define questions, each of which has merits and demerits. The following systems have been used successfully and are described briefly so that you can compare them.

The Open and Closed Model

CLOSED QUESTIONS:	all those which require a single word or very brief response, for which there is a single correct answer and the answer has been pre-determined by the questioner, e.g. 'What is the chemical formula for iron oxide?'
OPEN QUESTIONS:	all those which require an answer running to a sentence or more, where a variety of responses could be acceptable to the questions, and where there may be no 'correct' answer, e.g. 'How would you assess the character of Henry VIII?'

The Bloom—Turney Model

Source: Turney, C., 1977, *Sydney Micro Skills Series 2*, University of Sydney, based on Bloom's (1956) *Taxonomy of Educational Objectives*.

RECALL QUESTIONS:	ask pupils to remember information they have previously learned; e.g. 'What instrument did we use to make this measurement?'
COMPREHENSION QUESTIONS:	ask pupils to express ideas in their own words or to interpret the major elements in a piece of writing to make them more accessible to himself or someone else; e.g. 'If you believed that gods lived in every tree, how would you view the clearing of a forest?'
APPLICATION QUESTIONS:	ask the pupils to understand a general principle and apply it in new situations; e.g. 'What theorem would you use to find the size of this angle?'
ANALYSIS QUESTIONS:	ask the pupil to break down subject matter into its parts, and to study the nature of those parts and of the relationship between them; e.g. 'Why does Graham Greene choose to start the novel in that unusual way?'
SYNTHESIS QUESTIONS:	ask the pupils to build a new idea, plan or experiment; e.g. 'How would the view of the world put across in this play affect your attitude towards friendship and trust?'
EVALUATION QUESTIONS:	ask pupils to make judgments particularly about quality; e.g. 'To what extent are we convinced by the justice of the cause in this article, and how far are we just swayed by good writing?'

The Barnes Model

Source: Barnes, D. *et al*, 1969, *Language, the learner and the school*, Penguin Books.

FACTUAL QUESTIONS:	require pupils to give information or name a phenomenon, e.g. 'What happens when I switch on the current?'
REASONING QUESTIONS:	demand that pupils think aloud, to explain, interpret or construct a logically organised sequence (they may be open or closed), e.g. 'Why do you think migration benefits lemmings?'
OPEN, NON-REASONING QUESTIONS:	may or may not be factual, but leave room for a wide range of responses, e.g. 'Who can name any fraction?'
SOCIAL QUESTIONS:	include control questions and those designed to manage the group, e.g. 'Aren't we straying beyond the point?'

Finally in this section we can summarise some opinions about why questioning is a useful skill in teaching and learning.

WHY ASK QUESTIONS?

Some possible reasons are:
. . . to encourage pupils to talk constructively and on-task
. . . to signal an interest in hearing what pupils feel and think
. . . to stimulate interest and awaken curiosity
. . . to encourage a problem-solving approach to thinking and learning
. . . to help pupils externalise and verbalise knowledge
. . . to encourage 'thinking aloud' and exploratory approaches to tasks — the 'intuitive leap'
. . . to help pupils to learn from each other and to respect and evaluate each other's contributions
. . . to monitor the pupils' learning, its extent, level and deficiencies
. . . to deepen pupils' thinking levels and improve their ability to conceptualise

TOPIC C
SOME QUESTIONING SKILLS IN MORE DETAIL

In this section we are going to look at two skills of questioning in a little more detail; but before doing this we need to look at an issue which is of concern to all teachers. Are questioning skills the same across all subject disciplines, or are specific techniques applicable to modern linguists, English teachers or scientists etc.?

Obviously many basic skills are the same for everyone. Ability to distribute questions round the class, to isolate key questions, and to accept pupil responses — the kinds of skills described in Part 1 of this book — are universal.

The context of questioning does vary from subject to subject; and this can affect the way questions are formulated and distributed. For example, a linguist may use rapid-fire recall sequences to revise vocabulary, a mathematician may employ a similar technique to sharpen up pupils' concentration before a lesson gets fully under way. On the other hand, in a poetry lesson, an English teacher may want pupils to speculate about the content or style of verse; and so there may be more emphasis on thinking time, on extended answers and on pupils using their own ideas. In science many opportunities for questions to individual pupils are lost while an experiment is in progress; again the emphasis may be on speculation, but more structured theories may be required and a greater use of technical language.

That there are variations in style between subjects is clear from research, and the following brief extracts illustrate this with some typical questioning sequences across a range of curriculum areas reconstructed from the work reported in Sands and Kerry, 1981.[14] The reader may also find it useful to look at the volume in the Project's curriculum series of workbooks relating to his or her own subject area.*

A questioning sequence in French

Teacher: Last lesson we talked about numbers. Who can count to five?
Helen: Un, deux, trois, quatre, cinq.
Teacher: Good. Ann, go on.
Ann: Six, sept, huit, neuf, dix.
Teacher: Right, now who can say 'ten men' in French?
Mark: 'Dix hommes'
Teacher: Bien. Six houses?
Adam: Six maisons.
Teacher: Who can say 'three boys and two girls'?
Helen: Trois garçons et deux filles.
Teacher: Right, now we'll have some mental arithmetic. Andrew, six et trois?
Andrew: Neuf.

A questioning sequence in English

Teacher: In the poem 'Lark Ascending' how does Meredith capture the atmosphere of the lark's song? (Pause) Look at the text. (Longer pause)
Pauline: The form of the poem sounds like a lark.
Teacher: Can you describe more accurately what you mean by that?
Pauline: Well, the first section is very long. When you hear a skylark singing it seems to go on and on, there are no breaks in it. If you look at the beginning of the poem there are no full stops, it's just a very long sentence.
Teacher: That's true, good. What else besides the flow contributes to 'skylark sound' in the poem?
Elizabeth: I think the choice of words does.
Teacher: Go on, how does that work?
Elizabeth: Well, partly it's because he uses words that sound like bird song, for example 'chirrup', 'whistle' and so on. But there's more to it than that. I think he is saying that a lark keeps on singing like a running stream, so he builds up the trickling water images in line six onwards . . .

A questioning sequence in science

Teacher: If we wanted to compare insects with humans, how might we go about it?
James: You could look at the shape they took and compare the two.

*Details of this series are available from Trevor Kerry at the School of Education, Nottingham University, Nottingham NG7 2RD.

Teacher: Yes, any other ways?

Ann: You know what a person is like inside, you could dissect a butterfly or other insect and look at its inside.

Teacher: Fine — anything else?

John: You could watch its life-style and compare it with your own — what it eats, where it lives and so on.

Teacher: Well, there are three suggestions. They all mean we have to observe something. Let's take the butterfly specimen and deduce from it what we can. Teresa, can you tell me something about this creature, something which makes it different from us?

Teresa: It's got wings.

Teacher: Fine, what might that tell you about its lifestyle?

A questioning sequence in RE

Teacher: Why do you think it's wrong to steal?

Jane: Because it says so in the Bible.

Teacher: Well, it says a lot of things in the Bible, but they are not all relevant to today. Yet we still accept the command not to steal. Why?

Terry: If everyone went around stealing the world would be in chaos.

Teacher: That tells us that these laws may have a basis somewhere, that they weren't just plucked out of the air for no good reason. What was the basis do you think?

Ann: It was in how people behaved to one another in society as it was then.

Teacher: Yes, I think you're right. Some of these laws are social. So we may get laws from society, or handed down through religion. Do the two always say the same about things?

Sandra: No, the Church says you can only marry once but in our society you can get divorced.

Teacher: How do you make up your mind which is right when religion and society conflict.

Mark: Well, it all depends on whether you believe in religion to begin with. If you don't, and I don't, then there's no problem. You obey the law of the land and get on with your own life. If you do then conscience comes into it more.

Teacher: What exactly is 'a conscience'?

THE SKILL OF PROBING

In Part 1 probing was mentioned as one way in which teachers can improve pupils' answers to questions. Turney[15] has made a special study of how to probe more effectively, and the following paragraphs paraphrase his excellent work on this subject.

The purpose of probing is not simply 'to keep the conversation going'. Inexperienced teachers or students often feel that they have done well if they keep pupils talking regardless of the quality and relevance of the ideas being expressed. In Turney's view probing is questioning in order to sustain thinking. This probing serves a number of purposes:

(a) *To clarify*: here the pupil has to re-phrase a response or idea. In other words, to make it more accessible, e.g. 'What do you mean by the phrase "higher class"?'

(b) *To support a point of view*: the teacher can seek evidence to sustain an argument the pupil has advanced, e.g. 'What leads you to say that Shaw is prejudiced?'

(c) *To seek a degree of consensus*: here the teacher involves the rest of the class to test that they agree or disagree with the speaker and to make them feel involved, e.g. 'Which of you would share Jane's opinion?'

(d) *To test accuracy*: the respondent is asked to produce or suggest a proof of a statement made, e.g. 'How could you test your theory to show that it must hold true in all circumstances?'

(e) *To ensure relevance*: the teacher asks the pupil to demonstrate that a statement does, in fact, bear on the topic, e.g. 'Why do you think, John, that his age is important to the way he acts?'

(f) *To elicit examples*: this helps pupils to apply knowledge across a range of situations or to support a generalisation by specific citing of concrete examples, e.g. 'You say colour in animals can be a means of camouflage, Ann; what examples can you think of among moths, birds or fish?'

(g) *To raise a conciousness of complexity*: a pupil may stumble upon a good idea but be only partially aware of its significance. The teacher can help highlight the other facts by further questioning, e.g. 'Your religion will determine some of your moral attitudes, but what other experiences will also fashion this moral sense?'

The skill of probing helps teachers to get pupils to think more deeply and more widely, often about issues they themselves have raised. It is beneficial, too, in helping pupils to express more fully and more clearly what they have in mind. Practised over a long period with a class it will improve pupils' willingness to talk, their construction of responses and their grasp of thinking skills. *They will eventually probe their own thoughts without stimulus from the teacher, and the whole level of classroom dialogue will improve in quality.*

SEQUENCING AS A QUESTIONING SKILL

Finally we come to sequencing as a questioning skill. As a background to this topic we need to look at the knowledge pyramid discussed on page 35.

You may recall that to build up to higher levels of thinking one needed, it was said, to start from certain shared information before progressing towards ideas: data leads to concept which leads to generalisation.

In the same way a lesson in which all questions are at the highest levels is inconceivable at school level. In practice, teachers often begin with an assessment of where the class has reached in knowledge, and then they build on this to take the thinking one or more stages further, thus:

Teacher: Last time I told you the meaning of the Greek word 'apostle'. Do you remember what it was?

Julie: Sent.

Teacher: Right. It means someone who is sent. Who were the apostles, can you name some?

Michael: Paul, Peter, Matthew.

Ann: Judas Iscariot.

Philip: Philip.

Teacher: Now this word became linked with the idea of travelling the world preaching. Can anyone think of a good word to describe this activity?

James: Mission.

Teacher: Fine. In the age of the apostles we have the start of missions. Missionaries are often very dedicated — why do you think that is?

Fred: Well, they often feel very strongly called or chosen to do the job. They have a great sort of consciousness of their purpose.

Teacher: Is that always a good thing? It makes them very dedicated, but are there any disadvantages in this conviction?

Mandy: If you look at missionaries today I think it often clouds their judgment.

Teacher: How?

Mandy: Well, in South America, for example, it's difficult to untangle religion from politics . . .

In the discussion quoted above we see a progression in questioning from simple recall into levels of concept; and pupils are led quite quickly to reason, evaluate and analyse situations. *It is helpful, then, to think of questions not as isolated events so much as sequences which build up from small beginnings into endings which have cognitive significance.* In Activity 9 you are given the opportunity to practise this skill yourself. Finally, in Topic D there is a transcript for analysis, which will allow you to reflect upon the various skills you have learned throughout the whole of this workbook.

Activity 9:
Sequencing for cognitive demand

Plan a lesson on a topic of your choice. In your lesson plan (see Section 2 of Focus 2) devise a sequence of questions which gradually builds up from low level demand to higher level thinking from pupils.

Try to find an opportunity to teach this lesson. Record your impressions of how pupils respond to your question sequence and assess the quality of the ideas they produce.

TOPIC D
A TRANSCRIPT FOR ANALYSIS

Activity 10:
Transcript for analysis

Read through the transcript below. It is an extract from a lesson given by a teacher who used questioning as a major teaching method. Analyse the teacher's questions and the pupils' responses. Devise your own rating scale to do this; and/or make freehand comments as necessary.

N.B. *The purpose of the analysis is to discover the strengths and weaknesses of this teacher's lesson.*

Transcript

(Teacher shows prints of three large paintings)

Teacher: Can you tell me who any of these paintings are by?

Alan: The biggest one is a Van Gogh.

Teacher: Yes; and the other two?

Pauline: The city-scape looks as though it could also be Van Gogh.

Teacher: That's correct too. The last one is a bit different. What about that?

(The pupils talk among themselves discussing pros and cons; the teacher waits.)

Jeff: We can't be sure, but we're going to guess that it's also a Van Gogh. It's a shot in the dark.

Teacher: They are all by Van Gogh, actually. You were able to deduce who the artist was by a few clues, or so I gathered from your conversation. Why is it that we can know who the painter is just by looking at his painting?

Ann: I suppose it's what you might call 'style'.

Teacher: Yes, that's a good word. Every single painter has his own style of painting. Now we are going to try to find out and decide what are Van Gogh's basic characteristics of painting. What strikes you as the common factors in these paintings?

Alan: The look of the paint. The one in the middle looks sort of waxy. The other two are similar, though not identical.

Teacher: Yes, that's right. It's not just *how* the paint looks though, is it?

Mark: In the first picture the paint is very thickly applied.

Teacher: Where? Where is it applied thickly?

Ann: On the tree, in waves; and in the cornfield.

Teacher: Can you see it applied very sparingly in any of these paintings?

Alan: The technique is different in the city-scape, the paint is almost 'washy' in parts.

Teacher: Yes, that's right. What about here? This doorway? It's very sparingly applied, isn't it? And what special things about the painting technique contribute to his style?

Pauline: The colours are very bright, garish almost.

Teacher: Yes, that's right, the colours are bright. Do they, do you think, correspond to reality? Is that what a street looks like at night? Or a field? Is that what a field looks like?

Jeff: No, it's not accurate colour. The colour conveys a message.

Teacher: On the basis of that, what do you think the function of colour is? What does colour mean to Van Gogh?

Jeff: Is it perhaps mood?

Teacher: Yes, that's right, it reflects his mood. If the colour reflects his mood, what is Van Gogh's mood here? What do you think, Diane?

Diane: (almost inaudible) . . . bright for happiness.

Teacher: Well, yes, there are lots of bright colours. But red has a specific meaning for Van Gogh, red and purple. Yellow also had a specific meaning, it meant joy. So you were right in that it gives happiness, for him yellow means joy. But purple, round the doorway of the cafe: purple meant passion, some great passion. Given those clues what do you think the green means in this painting here?

Ann: Green for peace.

Teacher: Yes, that's right. We would describe the scene as 'pastoral'. Pastoral has overtones of peace, gentleness. So we have several contributions to style: how the paint is applied, its thickness or sparingness and the meaning behind the colours. Now I want to add another aspect of Van Gogh's style. How far does the earth reach up the painting?

Jeff: The horizon is near the top of the picture.

Teacher: Yes, three quarters of the way up. Now, in Van Gogh's paintings, in the majority of landscapes, the earth reaches most of the way up the painting.

Pauline: Why does it only reach half way up in the middle one?

Teacher: A good question. Can anyone begin to answer it for Pauline?

Jeff: Well, this is different. This is not a landscape inasmuch as he wants to portray basically this tree here.

Teacher: That's a very good answer: the tree takes the place of the landscape. Now, someone said that Van Gogh is one of the foremost men, and the first great man of temperament. Why do you think that was said?

Mark: He seems to use his painting as if he wants to pass messages. From what you say about yellow and purple and green etc., he seems to use the colours of paintings to illustrate moods.

Teacher: Yes. Temperament, because basically in his paintings he's not concerned with depicting reality so much as his own reaction towards that reality. What his feelings are, his temperament. Well, now, from what we've said you have been able to deduce something of Van Gogh's style by careful observation. So jot down now in your books the answer to this question: 'What steps would one take if one wanted to discover the basic characteristics of an artist's style?'. (Teacher writes question on blackboard.) Then we'll do something more practical.

Activity 11:
Assessing the effectiveness
of a questioning session

When you have analysed the transcript on the previous pages, set out the skills exhibited by the teacher. What criticisms of question technique would you make?

Skills	Criticism

COMMENTARY ON ACTIVITY 1 (page 7)

Key questions are:
1 Why do you think the Bible is sometimes called a library?
2 Suppose you were a librarian in charge of them, how would you arrange them on your shelves?
3 If you were a librarian you might use the classification idea. How would that work?

COMMENTARY ON ACTIVITY 2 (page 11)

Extract 1

YES. The teacher accepts a correct response and uses it to promote a follow-up question, building towards the point he wants to make.

Extract 2

NO. Fred experiments with a word he has heard but doesn't understand. The teacher feels he's just playing the fool or being clever and jumps on him, pressurising him to respond having once embarrassed him.

Extract 3

YES and NO. The teacher accepts and praises Peter's answers. He doesn't accept or reject John's directly, but allows disparaging comments to pass uncorrected so indicating to the pupil his approval of, and agreement with, them. Note, too, that Peter calls out his answer uninvited; and this may be undesirable.

Extract 4

YES. Julie's answer is only partly correct, but the teacher takes it up and uses her partial knowledge. He prompts her towards the right answer.

COMMENTARY ON ACTIVITY 3 (page 12)

1   Ambiguous as it stands, because we are unaware of the kinds of differences we are expected to look for. Better, perhaps: 'If it were true that Shakespeare's plays were written by Marlowe, what difference would this make to our assessment of Shakespeare as a writer?'. We should then be left to judge him by his other works.

2   Clear. (We can assume class has the appropriate technical language.)

3   In context, e.g. as a question arising out of a passage read aloud with the class, it would be clear enough.

4   There are too many long and technical words combined into a rambling sentence full of subordinate clauses for this to be clear. A test of its intelligibility would be if you could re-phrase it using simpler vocabulary. Can you?

COMMENTARY ON ACTIVITY 4 (page 14)

Teacher: A fairly open question, calling for evidence. Clear; and satisfactory vocabulary level. Directed to a specific pupil *after* the whole class has been alerted to it.

Peter: An apparently correct response, but lacking the evidence required so . . .

Teacher: The teacher probes to check on the pupil's understanding. This is shown up to be lacking by

Peter: the pupil's inadequate response to the simple reasoning question: Why?

Teacher: The teacher tries positively to reinforce Peter's contribution by making the connection between 'working' and 'working class' and opening the discussion to the whole class.

Marie: This works. Marie's response is correct and reasoned, but only up to a point. So the teacher again probes.

Teacher: In this longer input the teacher puts in unexplained technical terms. ('Registrar General'; 'classification'). However, she does allow adequate 'thinking time' for pupils to work out a series of alternative answers and some have followed the question.

Jo :)		Three contributions are forthcoming. The teacher interrupts
Ann:)		them to distinguish . . .
Bill :)		
Teacher:		between wages and salaries. But the question is poorly expressed and elicits no response. So . . .

(no response)

Neil:	Neil goes on with the list.
Teacher:	The teacher praises the new technical term but realises the rest of the class may not follow the implication so probes again.
Ian:	Ian's response is semi-humorous and the teacher . . .
Teacher:	feels threatened. Negative reinforcement. In fact it would have been better to use this contribution to ask why the store should choose that name.
Ann:	This pupil gives a partially correct answer so the teacher prompts. In the following series of questions . . .
Teacher:	the teacher leads Ann progressively towards an acceptable definition of
Ann:	'status' . . .
Teacher:	
Ann:	
Teacher:	
Ann:	
Teacher:	and then praises her for making the journey.
Ann:	Ann is therefore keen to keep answering.
Teacher:	The discussion has begun to clear some ground and the teacher, in a clear but more technical question, tries to raise the thinking level. Her generally supportive attitude encourages another contributor, Alan, to reveal something about himself . . .
Alan:	and his family.

NOTES

1 Barnes, D. et al, 1969, *Language, the learner and the school*, Penguin.
2 Pate, R.T. and Bremer, N. H., 1967, 'Guiding learning through skilful questioning', *The Elementary School Journal*, 69(8) 1967, pages 417–422.
3 Sands, M. K. and Kerry, T., 1981, *Mixed Ability Teaching*, Croom Helm.
4 Hannam, C., Smyth, P. and Stephenson, N., 1971, *Young teachers and reluctant learners*, Penguin.
5 Sutton, C. R. (ed.), 1981, *Communicating in the classroom*, Hodder and Stoughton.
6 Morris, D., 1978, *Manwatching*, Triad Panther.
7 Eggleston, J.F., Galton, M. and Jones, J.E., 1976, *Processes and Products of Science Teaching*, Schools Council Research Project: Macmillan Education.
8 Stevens, R., 1912, 'The question as a measure of efficiency in instruction: a critical study of classroom practice.' Teachers College Contributions to Education, no. 48.
9 Haynes, H. C., 1935, 'The relation of teacher intelligence, teacher experience and type of school to question types.' Doctoral dissertation, George Peabody College for Teachers.
10 Floyd, W., 1960, 'An analysis of oral questioning activity in selected Colorado primary classrooms.' Doctoral dissertation, Colorado State College.
11 Gallagher, J. J., 1965, 'Expressive thought by gifted children in the classroom.' *Elementary English*, vol. 42, pages 559–568.
12 Kerry, T., 1980, 'The demands made by RE on pupils' thinking'. *British Journal of Religious Education*, vol 3.2.
13 Gall, M. D., 1970, 'The use of questions in teaching.' *Review of Educational Research*, vol. 40, pages 707–721.
14 Sands, M. K. and Kerry, T., 1981, *Mixed Ability Teaching*, Croom Helm.
15 Turney, C., 1975, *Sydney Micro Skills Series 2*, University of Sydney.
16 Dunbar, R. E., 1970, 'An experimental study of the differential effects of certain hierarchically ordered stimulus questions upon subsequent task involvement.' Doctoral dissertation, University of Washington.

FURTHER READING A number of key texts have been referred to in the lists of references already cited. Your attention is drawn specifically to the following for further study:

Brown, G. A., 1977, *Microteaching*, Methuen.
Perrot, E., 1977, *Microteaching in higher education*, SRHE.
Turney, C., 1973, 1975, *Sydney Micro Skills Series 1 and 2*, University of Sydney.
Weigand, T., 1977, *Implementing teacher competencies*, Prentice Hall.